BONUS CHALLENGE

Take a close look at all the clowns shown here. Use them as a guide throughout your reading of the story. When you have
solved all the other story puzzles, see if you can spot the six differences between these clowns and the clowns shown on the last
page of the book. If you do, you'll become an honorary member of the Colossally Clever Carnival Caper Case-Cracking Club!

ARE YOU A PUZZLE MASTER?

One of the most spectacular carnivals in the world is the Thirteen Clown Carnival, and it has just been bought by Signor Butteroni. He has invited his nephew, Tom, along with Susan, Matt, and their little dog Patches to come to the opening.

But soon after arriving, they discover something strange is going on. Confusion and chaos seem to be everywhere. Who or what is responsible? That's what they and *you* must find out.

Join Tom, Susan, Matt, Patches, and Signor Butteroni as they explore all the exciting carnival rides in their search for an answer. It's the adventure of a lifetime for our heroes as they try to solve all the challenges, mazes, and puzzles of this great carnival mystery—with your help.

You'll find the answers at the back of the book.

A Reader's Digest Kids Book
Published by The Reader's Digest Association, Inc.
Produced by Joshua Morris Publishing, Inc.
Copyright © 1993 John Speirs
Storyline, Gill Speirs
All rights reserved. Unauthorized reproduction,
in any manner, is prohibited.
Printed in Singapore.
10 9 8 7 6 5 4 3 2 1

Library of Congress Cataloging in Publication Data
Speirs, John.
  The great carnival caper / John Speirs.
    p.   cm. — (Puzzle masters)
  Summary: A series of picture puzzles in which the reader helps
three young Puzzle Masters and their dog locate carnival
entertainers, animals, and other attractions, decode messages, and
find the villain responsible for wreaking havoc with the carnival.
  ISBN 0-89577-453-4
  1. Picture puzzles—Juvenile literature.   2. Maze puzzles—
Juvenile literature.   [1. Picture puzzles.   2. Puzzles.]
I. Title.   II. Series.
GV1507.P47S68 1993
793.73—dc20   92-38171
                                                       CIP
                                                        AC

Reader's
Digest

John Speirs
PUZZLE MASTERS®

The Great Carnival Caper

Reader's Digest Kids
PLEASANTVILLE, N.Y. – MONTREAL

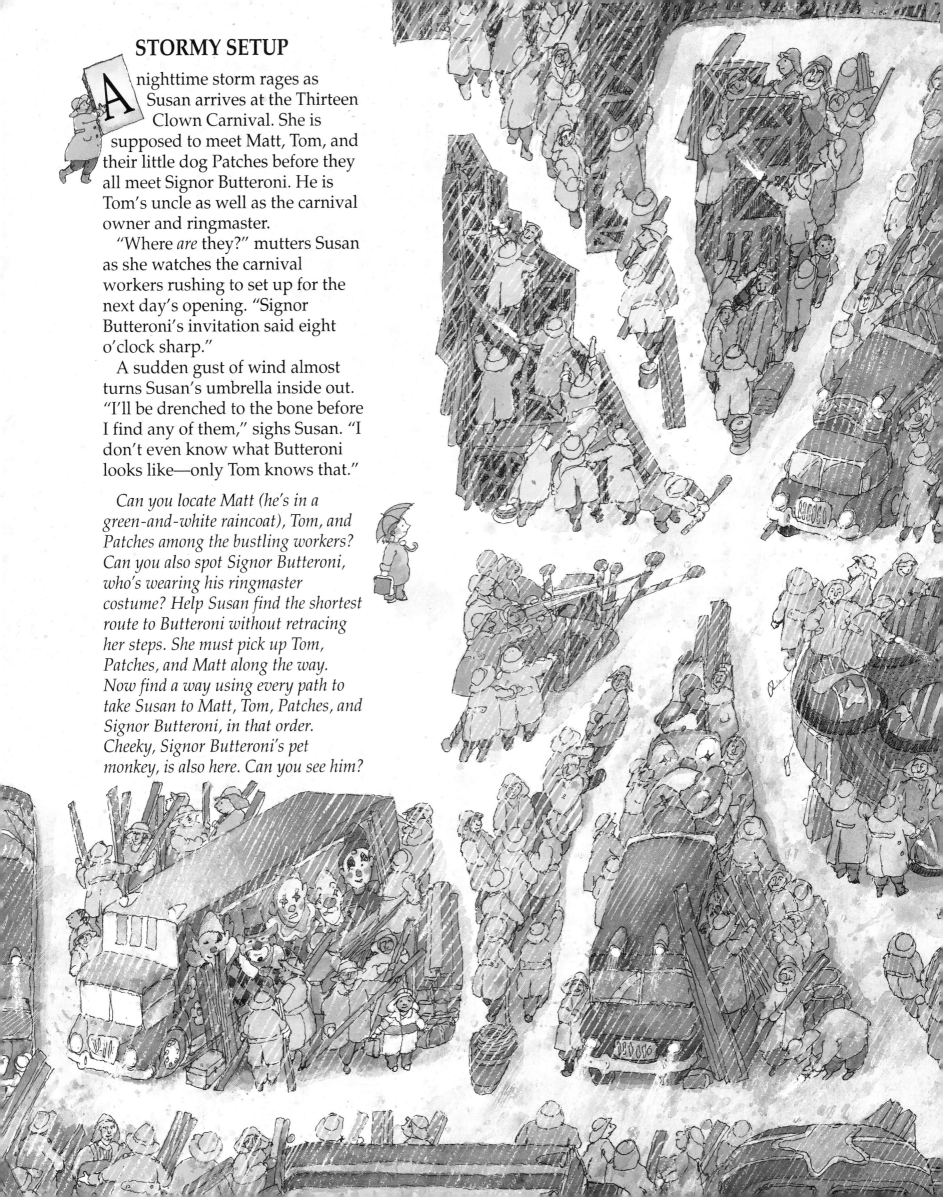

STORMY SETUP

A nighttime storm rages as Susan arrives at the Thirteen Clown Carnival. She is supposed to meet Matt, Tom, and their little dog Patches before they all meet Signor Butteroni. He is Tom's uncle as well as the carnival owner and ringmaster.

"Where *are* they?" mutters Susan as she watches the carnival workers rushing to set up for the next day's opening. "Signor Butteroni's invitation said eight o'clock sharp."

A sudden gust of wind almost turns Susan's umbrella inside out. "I'll be drenched to the bone before I find any of them," sighs Susan. "I don't even know what Butteroni looks like—only Tom knows that."

Can you locate Matt (he's in a green-and-white raincoat), Tom, and Patches among the bustling workers? Can you also spot Signor Butteroni, who's wearing his ringmaster costume? Help Susan find the shortest route to Butteroni without retracing her steps. She must pick up Tom, Patches, and Matt along the way. Now find a way using every path to take Susan to Matt, Tom, Patches, and Signor Butteroni, in that order. Cheeky, Signor Butteroni's pet monkey, is also here. Can you see him?

A MYSTERIOUS MESS AND MESSAGE

"Just look at my wagon!" says Signor Butteroni. He is very upset.

Glad to be out of the rain, Tom, Matt, and Susan glance around as they sip cups of hot chocolate.

"It looks like someone has gone through all your things, Uncle," says Tom.

"Just look at how everything has been broken," adds Susan.

"Who would do this? And why?" asks Matt. "I just hope nothing's missing."

"Oddly enough," sighs Butteroni, "the only things taken are a picture of the thirteen clowns and my strongbox."

"What's in the strongbox?" asks Susan.

"The carnival blueprints," says Butteroni. "As you know, this is no ordinary carnival, and it has its own special plans of construction."

Butteroni picks up a piece of paper and smiles for the first time. "I've asked my old friend, Inspector Clue, to help out on the case. He sent me this telegram."

"Wow!" says Matt. "Clue's the greatest detective in the world!"

"That's right," says Signor Butteroni. "I just wish I could understand all of his telegram."

Despite what Susan said, there are fifteen things undamaged in Butteroni's wagon. Can you find them? And can you make sense of Inspector Clue's telegram?

LOST IN THE FUNHOUSE

"I want you to meet my thirteen clowns," Butteroni says proudly as they enter the funhouse through its gaping jaws.

Matt looks around in wonder. "How did you get all these things to stick to the ceiling?" he asks.

"That's a carnival secret, Matt!" says Signor Butteroni, smiling. Then he takes a closer look inside the funhouse and frowns. "Oh, no!" he cries. "What has happened here? Who has turned some of these things the right way up?"

"Do you think someone is trying to harm the carnival, Uncle?" asks Tom. "First your wagon, and now this."

"Oh, dear!" says Butteroni. "It certainly looks that way."

"I hope Inspector Clue is working hard to find an answer," says Susan. "I wish we knew just what the great detective is up to now."

Find thirty or more objects inside the funhouse that are not *upside-down. There are three paintings on the walls that seem identical—but aren't. Can you spot five differences between the paintings?*

WHEEL'S-EYE VIEW

"If Tom is right and someone *is* trying to harm my carnival," says Signor Butteroni, "we'll be able to get a clearer view from up here on the Ferris wheel."

"Doesn't it take your breath away?" says Susan.

"Yes, yes," nervously gasps Matt, trying not to look down.

"We can certainly see what's wrong from here," says Susan, scanning the ground. "The carnival workers are getting things very muddled."

Tom agrees. "Some of the rides and sideshows seem oddly put together."

"If only the blueprints hadn't been taken!" cries Butteroni. "And the three-seat, three-wheeled Clowncycle is missing. What *else* could possibly go wrong?"

The words are barely out of Butteroni's mouth when the wind whips up and blows his top hat off. "I knew I spoke too soon," he sighs, watching the hat drift far away. "That's the only top hat I have."

Can you find twenty-five things wrong with the carnival? And where is Butteroni's top hat?

BLIMP BLITZ

"What a great way to tell everybody about the carnival," says Susan, as she and the others send flyers fluttering down to the crowd below. "This blimp can be seen for miles around. It's really worked, too. Just look at the crowd pouring in!"

"You know, those clowns have great faces, Uncle," says Tom, admiring their pictures on the blimp. "No wonder they're the stars of the carnival."

"Among many others," says Signor Butteroni, beaming. "Some of my wonderful sideshow performers are listed on the side of the blimp."

"Where are they?" asks Matt, peering at the crowd.

"I can't see them too well from here," says Signor Butteroni. "But I know they're among the crowd. The clowns are there as well."

"Whoever is causing all your trouble is probably down there, too," adds Susan.

"I suspect you're right, Susan," says Butteroni.

"Perhaps we should be down there with Inspector Clue searching for the troublemaker," says Tom. "There's so much that could go wrong."

Help the blimp riders spot each of the carnival clowns below. Then look through the crowd for the sideshow performers listed on the blimp.

The Thirteen
Clown Carnival
presents

Fire Eater
Strongman
Live Mermaid
Human Cannonball
Tattooed Man
Bearded Lady
Puppet Show
Human Rubberband
Four Dancers
Fat Lady
Juggler

TORNADO TWISTER

The moment Tom, Susan, Matt, and Butteroni arrive at the next ride, the Tornado Twister, they jump into a car and buckle themselves in. As the car starts to shoot up a steep slope, Matt asks, "What's so special about this roller coaster?"

"This is no roller coaster," answers Signor Butteroni. "This is the famous Tornado Twister! It can move up or down, switching off onto different tracks with the sudden speed of a—"

"Tornado!" chime in Susan, Tom, and Matt together, laughing.

Matt sees the carnival workers on the scaffolding. "This ride *is* safe, isn't it?" he asks.

"Oh, yes," says Butteroni. "Those are just my safety inspectors. They're checking the Tornado Twister."

"Have you seen a wrench and a saw?" calls out an inspector.
"No," answers Butteroni. "Sorry I can't help."
Then, pointing, Susan shouts, "Look! There's a man acting very suspiciously in the car at the finish—and Patches almost caught him!" Louder, she yells, "Stay with him, Patches! We'll catch up!"

The Tornado Twister has sixteen stops. From start to finish, can you work your way through the ride to all sixteen stops, arriving at each one only once? Besides a wrench and saw, the safety inspectors have mislaid a hammer, screwdriver, shovel, pliers, and electric drill on the scaffolding. Can you find all the tools? Which two safety inspectors are twins?

BUMPER CARS

"There's Patches!" says Tom, pointing toward the brave little dog now scampering between bumper cars.

"We'd better try to catch up with him," calls Susan, starting to run after the dog.

"Be quick!" urges Butteroni, who sees the suspicious figure disappearing on the other side of the bumper cars. "But be careful!" he adds, joining the chase.

"Don't worry, Patches," shouts Susan, dashing and dodging through the cars. "We're close behind you!"

Huffing after them is Butteroni. "This detective business is hard work!" he says, pausing to catch his

breath. "Oh, if only Inspector Clue were here to help us!"

Find a pathway from Butteroni and the children, through the bumper cars, to Patches. Continue until you reach the exit where the suspicious figure was last seen. To test your skill, return to the beginning and find a new route to the same exit by jumping from car to car. You must jump from one star and stripe to another star and stripe of the same color. Sometimes you will have to change colors by jumping along the length of a car to a star and stripe of different colors. Which two bumper cars are identical? And where's Cheeky?

RAINBOW ROCKET

"We've lost Patches *and* the man he was chasing!" says Tom glumly.

"Don't lose hope," says Signor Butteroni. "Let's take a ride on my Rainbow Rocket. Maybe we can see them from up there."

Susan quickly climbs into a green rocket, Tom and Matt jump into a yellow rocket behind hers, while Butteroni settles into a blue rocket.

"We're flying now," says Tom, pulling the steering wheel up. The rocket he and Matt are in suddenly zooms skyward.

"You'll never catch me!" shouts Susan over her shoulder.

"I'll catch all of you!" yells Butteroni with a loud laugh from the rear.

"Hey! Look at those flags!" says Matt. "There are letters on them."

"That's strange," says Butteroni. "I don't remember this ride having any letters before."

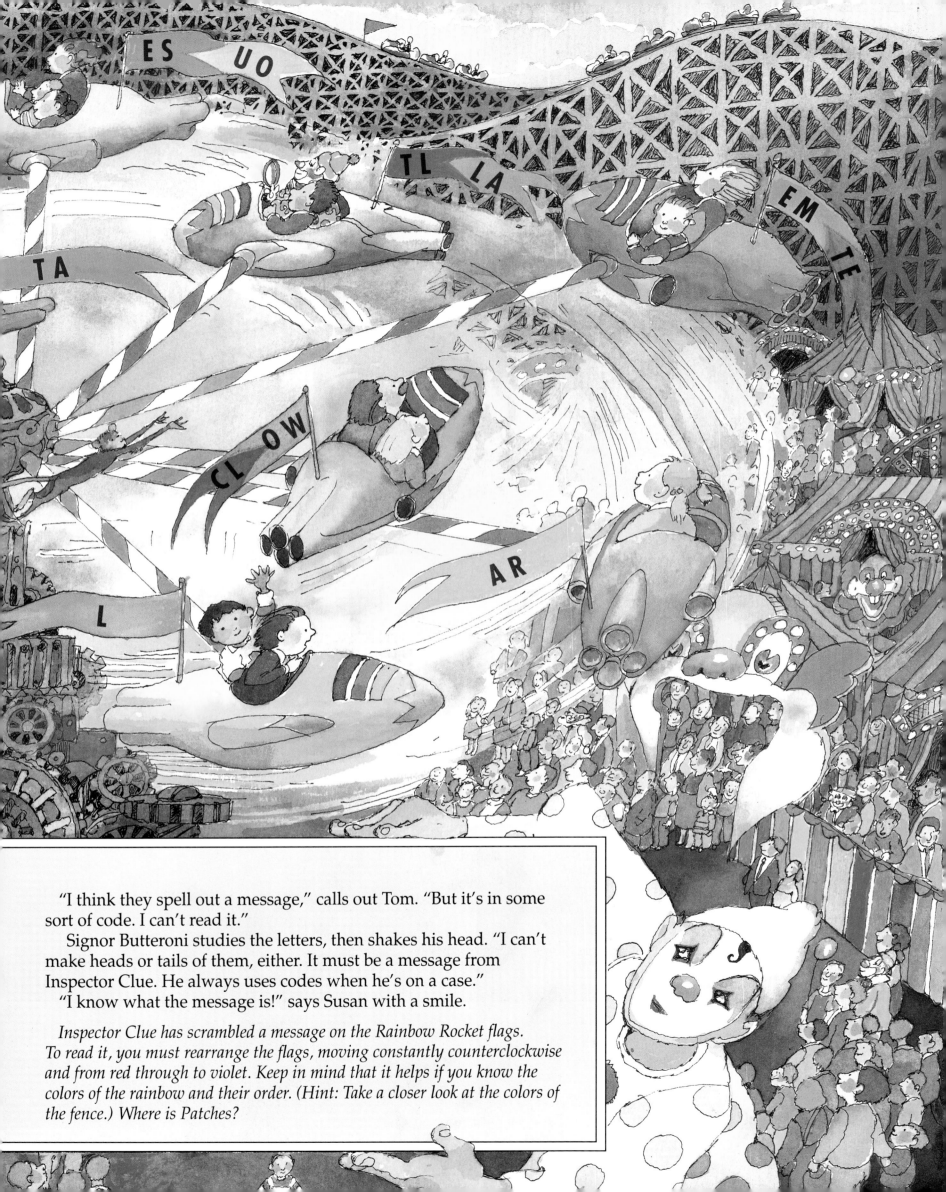

"I think they spell out a message," calls out Tom. "But it's in some sort of code. I can't read it."

Signor Butteroni studies the letters, then shakes his head. "I can't make heads or tails of them, either. It must be a message from Inspector Clue. He always uses codes when he's on a case."

"I know what the message is!" says Susan with a smile.

Inspector Clue has scrambled a message on the Rainbow Rocket flags. To read it, you must rearrange the flags, moving constantly counterclockwise and from red through to violet. Keep in mind that it helps if you know the colors of the rainbow and their order. (Hint: Take a closer look at the colors of the fence.) Where is Patches?

BALANCING ACT

Signor Butteroni, Tom, Susan, and Matt move swiftly through the carnival. They must track down each of the clowns to pass on Inspector Clue's message.

"At last," says Butteroni, "we might be getting to the bottom of this caper."

"Uh-oh, Uncle," cries Tom, looking up. "I don't think it's over yet."

High above them are nineteen acrobats teetering on a tightrope. They seem to be having great trouble keeping their balance.

"I've always wanted to walk on a tightrope," says Matt softly. "Even falling into the net must be fun."

"I'm not so sure," says Susan, letting out a gasp when the acrobat on the unicycle wobbles. "He's having a hard time holding his balance," she whispers.

"No wonder," says Butteroni. "They're missing an umbrella. Even the slightest change in costume can cause problems."

Take a closer look at all the acrobats balancing on the man on the unicycle. Everyone and everything on the left should be a perfect mirror image of everyone and everything on the right. Besides the umbrella, can you spot eight differences? Can you also pick out Butteroni, Tom, Susan, Matt, Patches, and Cheeky below?

CRAZY CAROUSEL

"Finally, the carousel!" says Tom excitedly.

"Let's go on it!" urges Matt.

"Wait!" cries Butteroni gloomily. "It's a disaster! My beautiful Thirteen Clown Carnival will be laughed at throughout the world, and I shall be ruined! Just look at the animal rides—they're in complete chaos!"

"Your uncle's right, Tom," says Susan. "I can see the head of a rhinoceros on top of a horse's front legs attached to a fish's tail. All the other rides are mixed up, too."

"But everyone is having so much fun!" says Tom.

"They all think the rides are *meant* to be muddled up like this," adds Matt.

"Maybe so, but we still must find the blueprints to put this carousel back together correctly," says Butteroni. Then, in an impatient voice, he asks, "And where is Inspector Clue? He was supposed to meet us here."

"I think he's already been here," says Susan, pointing to the flashing lights above the carousel. "That must be another message from him."

Can you make up and name seven complete animals from the mixed-up ones you see? Can you figure out Inspector Clue's message on top of the carousel? (Hint: His message is fourteen words long.)

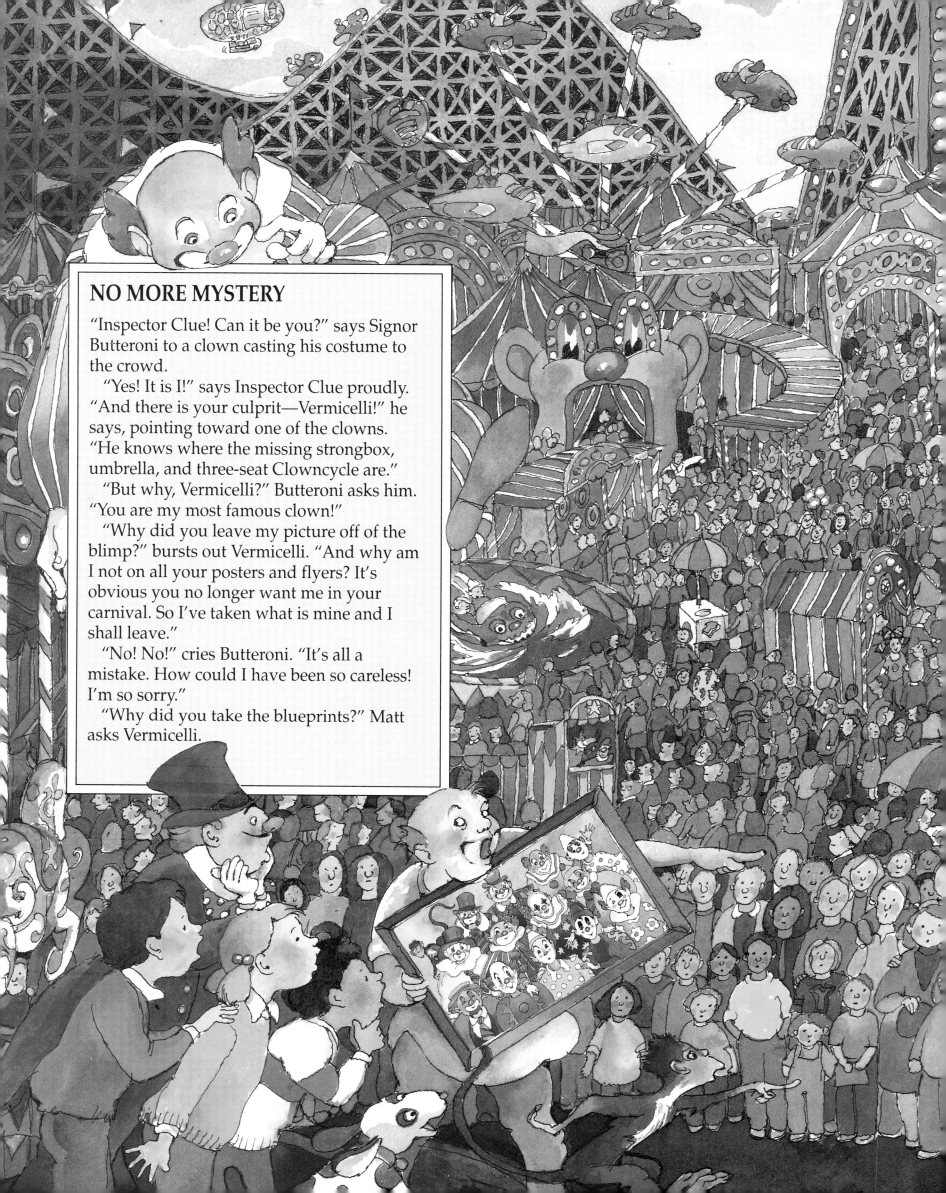

NO MORE MYSTERY

"Inspector Clue! Can it be you?" says Signor Butteroni to a clown casting his costume to the crowd.

"Yes! It is I!" says Inspector Clue proudly. "And there is your culprit—Vermicelli!" he says, pointing toward one of the clowns. "He knows where the missing strongbox, umbrella, and three-seat Clowncycle are."

"But why, Vermicelli?" Butteroni asks him. "You are my most famous clown!"

"Why did you leave my picture off of the blimp?" bursts out Vermicelli. "And why am I not on all your posters and flyers? It's obvious you no longer want me in your carnival. So I've taken what is mine and I shall leave."

"No! No!" cries Butteroni. "It's all a mistake. How could I have been so careless! I'm so sorry."

"Why did you take the blueprints?" Matt asks Vermicelli.

"I didn't mean to take them," answers the clown sadly. "I just took back the strongbox I had loaned to Signor Butteroni."

"Then why did you break so many things in my wagon?" asks Butteroni.

"I didn't mean to break them," says Vermicelli. "I'm just so clumsy. I'm sorry. Do you still want me in your carnival?"

"Of course!" answers Butteroni. "What good is a Thirteen Clown Carnival with twelve clowns!"

"Now that the mystery is solved," says Tom, "let's enjoy the best carnival I know!"

Can you pick out Vermicelli among the thirteen clowns? Can you spot Inspector Clue's bowtie, cap, white shirt, jacket, pants, red wig, false clown nose, shoes and striped socks, and magnifying glass? And where are the strongbox, umbrella, and three-seat Clowncycle that Vermicelli took? Finally, did you notice that Clue in his clown disguise and the thirteen real clowns are shown in every carnival scene? Go back and see if you can find them.

PUZZLE ANSWERS

Stormy Setup

Matt, Tom, Signor Butteroni, Patches, and Cheeky are circled in BLACK. The BLUE path is the shortest way for Susan to reach Butteroni while picking up Tom, Patches, and Matt without retracing her steps. Following the RED path will take you through every path between Susan and Butteroni while picking up Matt, Tom, and Patches in that order. Inspector Clue and a picture of Signor Vermicelli are each circled in YELLOW.

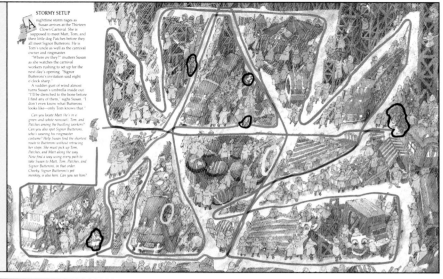

A Mysterious Mess and Message

The fifteen undamaged things are circled in BLACK. To unscramble Inspector Clue's telegram, read the letters from right to left, bottom to top. The whole message reads as follows: DEAR SIGNOR BUTTERONI, I ACCEPT THE CASE. I AM ARRIVING THIS EVENING TO HELP, AND I WILL BE IN DISGUISE. SIGNED, INSPECTOR CLUE. P.S. REMEMBER—WHERE THERE'S A CLUE, THERE'S A SOLUTION. All thirteen real clowns are shown in the picture held by a cloaked Signor Vermicelli, circled in BLUE. Inspector Clue is circled in BLUE.

Lost in the Funhouse

The objects that are not upside-down are circled in BLACK. The five differences between the three paintings are circled in BLUE. Signor Vermicelli and Inspector Clue are each circled in RED.

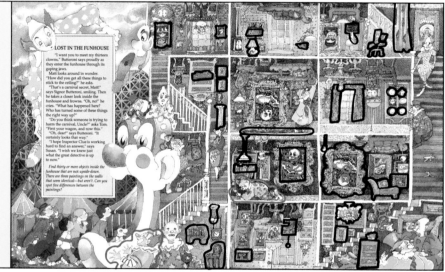

Wheel's-Eye View

The twenty-five things that are wrong with the carnival are circled in BLACK. Signor Butteroni's top hat is circled in BLUE. Signor Vermicelli and Inspector Clue are each circled in RED.

Blimp Blitz

The twelve carnival clowns shown on the blimp are circled in BLACK below in the crowd. The fire eater, strongman, live mermaid, human cannonball, tattooed man, bearded lady, juggler, human rubberband, four dancers, fat lady, and puppet show are all circled in BLUE. Signor Vermicelli and Inspector Clue are each circled in RED.

Tornado Twister

The RED path shows one way you can work through the sixteen stops—numbered in sequence here—of the ride while arriving at each stop only once. Can you find any other ways? The mislaid hammer, screwdriver, saw, shovel, pliers, electric drill, and wrench are circled in BLACK. The twin safety inspectors are circled in YELLOW. Signor Vermicelli and Inspector Clue are each circled in BLUE.

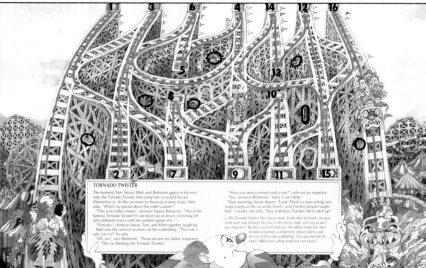

Bumper Cars

The WHITE dotted path shows a narrow, winding way through the bumper cars to Patches and then to the exit. The YELLOW line shows how to jump from bumper car to bumper car until you reach the exit. The two identical bumper cars are circled in RED. Cheeky is circled in BLUE. Signor Vermicelli and Inspector Clue are each circled in BLACK.

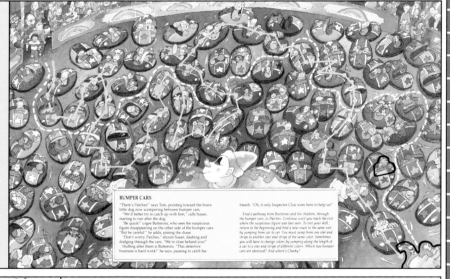

Rainbow Rocket

The correct order of the rainbow's colors can be seen on the fence. With the fence colors as a guide, the correct order of the rainbow's colors shown on the flags is red, red-orange, orange, orange-yellow, yellow, yellow-green, green, green-blue, blue, blue-dark blue, dark blue, dark blue-violet, and violet. Following that color order and reading the letters on the thirteen flags in a counterclockwise direction will produce this message from Inspector Clue: MEET ME AT THE CAROUSEL. BRING ALL THE CLOWNS. Patches is circled in RED. Signor Vermicelli and Inspector Clue are each circled in BLACK.

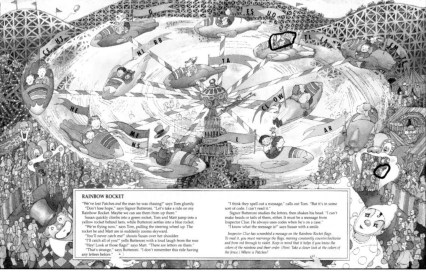

Balancing Act

The eight differences, besides the umbrella, are circled in RED. Signor Butteroni, Tom, Susan, Matt, Patches, and Cheeky are circled in YELLOW. Signor Vermicelli and Inspector Clue are each circled in BLACK.

Crazy Carousel

Seven complete animals can be made from the mixed-up ones seen on the carousel. They are a zebra, pig, giraffe, lion, elephant, rooster, and tiger. Their parts are numbered in RED, with the same number appearing on all the parts of that particular animal. You can figure out Inspector Clue's fourteen-word message by starting at the lower left of the two rows of lights, moving diagonally up-and-down once across, and then moving diagonally up-and-down a second time across from the top left. The message reads as follows: AT LAST IT ALL ADDS UP. I NOW KNOW WHO AND WHY. HOORAY. CLUE. Signor Vermicelli and Inspector Clue are each circled in BLACK.

No More Mystery

Take a good look at the picture of the thirteen real clowns that Inspector Clue is holding, then scan all the clowns, including the one standing upper left. Signor Vermicelli is the clown circled in BLUE. Inspector Clue's bowtie, cap, white shirt, jacket, pants, red wig, false clown nose, shoes and striped socks, and magnifying glass are circled in YELLOW. The three things Vermicelli took—the three-seat, three-wheeled Clowncycle, the strongbox, and the umbrella—are circled in BLACK.